Healing for Today Scripture Journal

AMY KEESEE FREUDIGER

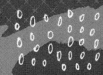

MW00625419

This Journal Belongs to:

Healing for Today Scripture Journal
Copyright © 2022 by Amy Keesee Freudiger

Unless otherwise noted, all Scriptures quoted are from the New International Version (NIV) of the Holy Bible®, NIV®. Copyright © 1973, 1978, 1984, 2011 by Biblica, Inc.® Used by permission. All rights reserved worldwide.

Scriptures marked (NLT) are from the New Living Translation® of the Holy Bible. Copyright © 1996, 2004, 2007, 2013 by Tyndale House Foundation. Used by permission of Tyndale House Publishers, Inc., Carol Stream, Illinois 60188. All rights reserved. New Living, NLT, and the New Living Translation logo are registered trademarks of Tyndale House Publishers.

Scriptures marked (MSG) are from The Message Version of the Holy Bible. Copyright © 1993, 1994, 1995, 1996, 2000, 2001, 2002. Used by permission of NavPress Publishing Group.

Scriptures marked (TLB) are from The Living Bible. Copyright © 1971 by Tyndale House Foundation. Used by permission of Tyndale House Publishers Inc., Carol Stream, Illinois 60188. All rights reserved. The Living Bible, TLB, and the The Living Bible logo are registered trademarks of Tyndale House Publishers.

ISBN 978-1-7375555-4-4

Published by Honest Beauty Publishing.
Printed in the United States of America.

All rights reserved. No part of this book may be used or reproduced by any means, graphic, electronic or mechanical, including photocopying, recording, taping, or by any information storage retrieval system without the written permission of the publisher, except in the case of brief quotations embodied in critical articles and reviews.

Author's note: I do not capitalize the name "satan," because I do not ascribe him even that small honor.

Cover Design and Graphic Design: Establishr.co.

A Note from the Author

Dear Friend,

I have seen the power of God's Word change even the worst of circumstances, including sickness and disease. I myself was healed supernaturally, and it all started with speaking God's Word out loud daily, as I share in my book **Healed Overnight: Five Steps to Accessing Supernatural Healing**. I have also seen the compound effect of focusing on God's Word for a 30-day period of time, as I detail in **The 30-Day Healing Dare Devotional**.

In this journal, you will find a month's worth of healing Scriptures to meditate on and journal about. Or if you prefer, take one Scripture per week for 30 weeks. I challenge you to put your name in the Scripture, where applicable, and say it out loud. Make it personal, because God's promises are for you today. Pray through each Scripture and ask the Holy Spirit to show you how it applies to your life.

There is a place for you to journal your reflections and thoughts. Then, there is a place for you to reflect on what you are grateful for, because gratitude is healing to our minds and bodies! Finally, use the prayer box to write directly to God about what's on your heart.

At the end, there's a section to record answered prayers and also things God speaks to you.

I pray this healing scripture journal will aid you as you seek God's promises concerning healing. Many blessings to you!

-Amy

But he was pierced for our transgressions, he was crushed for our iniquities; the punishment that brought us peace was on him, and by his wounds we are healed.

ISAIAH 53:5

Reflection

_____
_____
_____
_____
_____
_____
_____
_____
_____
_____
_____
_____
_____
_____
_____
_____
_____
_____
_____
_____
_____

WHAT I'M Thankful FOR

⟫⟫⟫ My Prayer ⟪⟪⟪

It stands to reason, doesn't it, that if the alive-and-present God who raised Jesus from the dead moves into your life, he'll **do the same thing in you that he did in Jesus**, bringing **you alive** to himself? When God lives and breathes in you (and he does, as surely as he did in Jesus), you *are delivered from that dead life*. With his Spirit living in you, *your body will be as alive as Christ's*!

Isaiah 53:5

Date: ~~~~~~~~~~~~~~~~

~~~~~~~~~~~~~~~~

Reflection

_____

_____

_____

_____

_____

_____

_____

_____

_____

_____

_____

_____

_____

_____

_____

_____

_____

_____

_____

_____

_____

_____

WHAT I'M Thankful FOR

My Prayer

God is **not human,**
that he should lie,
not a human being, that
he should change his mind.

Does he speak and
then not act?

Does he promise and not
fulfill?

NUMBERS 23:19

Date: ~~~~~~~~~~~~~~~~~~

Reflection

_____
_____
_____
_____
_____
_____
_____
_____
_____
_____
_____
_____
_____
_____
_____
_____
_____
_____

WHAT I'M Thankful FOR

My Prayer

Every **good** and **perfect** **gift** is from **above**, coming down from the Father of the heavenly lights, who does **not change** like shifting shadows.

James 1:17

Date: 〰〰〰〰〰〰
〰〰〰〰〰〰

Reflection

WHAT I'M Thankful FOR

_____
_____
_____

_____
_____
_____
_____
_____

⟫⟫⟫ My Prayer ⟪⟪⟪

I have given you authority to trample on snakes and scorpions and to overcome all the power of the enemy; nothing will harm you.

LUKE 10:19

Date: ~~~~~~~~~~~~~~~~~~~

~~~~~~~~~~~~~~~~~~~

Reflection

_____

_____

_____

_____

_____

_____

_____

_____

_____

_____

_____

_____

_____

_____

_____

_____

_____

_____

_____

_____

WHAT I'M Thankful FOR

My Prayer

Praise the Lord, my soul, and **forget not** all his **benefits**-who **forgives** all your sins and **heals all your diseases**

Psalm 103:2-3

Date: ～～～～～～～～～
～～～～～～～～～

Reflection

_____
_____
_____
_____
_____
_____
_____
_____
_____
_____
_____
_____
_____
_____
_____
_____
_____
_____
_____
_____
_____
_____

WHAT I'M Thankful FOR

My Prayer

Dear friend, I pray that you may enjoy **good health** and that all may go well with you, even as your soul is getting along well.

3 JOHN 1:2

Date: ~~~~~~~~~~~~~~~~
~~~~~~~~~~~~~~~~

Reflection

_____
_____
_____
_____
_____
_____
_____
_____
_____
_____
_____
_____
_____
_____
_____
_____
_____
_____
_____
_____
_____

WHAT I'M Thankful FOR

My Prayer

He will take our weak mortal bodies and change them into **glorious bodies** like his own, using the same power with which he will bring everything under his control.

Philippians 3:21 (NLT)

Date: ～～～～～～～

～～～～～～～

Reflection

_____

_____

_____

_____

_____

_____

_____

_____

_____

_____

_____

_____

_____

_____

_____

_____

_____

_____

_____

_____

WHAT I'M Thankful FOR

My Prayer

Yet he **did not waver** through unbelief regarding the **promise of God**, but was **strengthened** in his faith and gave glory to God, being **fully persuaded** that God had **power** to do what he had **promised.**

ROMANS 4:20-21

Date: ~~~~~~~~~~~~~~~
~~~~~~~~~~~~~~~

Reflection

_____
_____
_____
_____
_____
_____
_____
_____
_____
_____
_____
_____
_____
_____
_____
_____
_____
_____
_____
_____
_____

WHAT I'M Thankful FOR

My Prayer

He sent out his word
and healed them;
he rescued them
from the grave.

PSALM 107:20

Reflection

_____
_____
_____
_____
_____
_____
_____
_____
_____
_____
_____
_____
_____
_____
_____
_____
_____
_____
_____
_____

WHAT I'M Thankful FOR

My Prayer

When Jesus came into Peter's house, he saw Peter's mother-in-law lying in bed with a fever. He **touched her** hand and the **fever left** her, and she got up and began to wait on him.

When evening came, many who were demon-possessed were brought to him, and he drove out the spirits with a word and **healed all the sick**. This was to fulfill what was spoken through the prophet Isaiah:

"He took up our **infirmities** and bore our **diseases**."

Matthew 8:14–17

Date: ~~~~~~~~~~

~~~~~~~~~~

Reflection

_____

_____

_____

_____

_____

_____

_____

_____

_____

_____

_____

_____

_____

_____

_____

_____

_____

_____

_____

_____

_____

_____

WHAT I'M ~~~
Thankful
~~~ FOR

_____
_____
_____
_____
_____

_____
_____
_____
_____
_____

⟩⟩⟩— My Prayer —⟨⟨⟨

They will have no fear
of bad news;
their hearts are
steadfast, trusting
in the Lord.

PSALM 112:7

Date: ~~~~~~~~~~~~~~
~~~~~~~~~~~~~~

Reflection

_____
_____
_____
_____
_____
_____
_____
_____
_____
_____
_____
_____
_____
_____
_____
_____
_____
_____
_____
_____

WHAT I'M Thankful FOR

My Prayer

Jesus turned and saw her. "Take heart, **daughter**," he said, "**your faith** has **healed you**." And the woman was **healed at that moment**.

Matthew 9:22

Date: ~~~~~~~~~~~~

~~~~~~~~~~~~

Reflection

WHAT I'M Thankful FOR

⟫⟫⟫ My Prayer ⟪⟪⟪

Lord my God, I called to you for help, and you healed me.

PSALM 30:2

Date: ~~~~~~~~~~

Reflection

_____
_____
_____
_____
_____
_____
_____
_____
_____
_____
_____
_____
_____
_____
_____
_____
_____
_____
_____
_____

WHAT I'M Thankful FOR

My Prayer

How God anointed Jesus of Nazareth with the Holy Spirit and power, and how he went around doing good and healing all who were under the power of the devil, because God was with him.

ACTS 10:38

Date: ～～～～～～～

～～～～～～～

Reflection

_____
_____
_____
_____
_____
_____
_____
_____
_____
_____
_____
_____
_____
_____
_____
_____
_____
_____
_____

WHAT I'M Thankful FOR

My Prayer

Not at all! Let **God be true**, and every human being a liar.

Romans 3:4a

Date: ~~~~~~~~~~~

~~~~~~~~~~~

Reflection

_____

_____

_____

_____

_____

_____

_____

_____

_____

_____

_____

_____

_____

_____

_____

_____

_____

_____

_____

_____

WHAT I'M Thankful FOR

_____
_____
_____
_____
_____
_____
_____
_____
_____
_____
_____

⊁≡ My Prayer ≡⊱

_____
_____
_____
_____
_____
_____
_____
_____
_____
_____

Now faith is confidence in what we hope for and assurance about what we do not see.

HEBREWS 11:1

Reflection

_____

_____

_____

_____

_____

_____

_____

_____

_____

_____

_____

_____

_____

_____

_____

_____

_____

WHAT I'M Thankful FOR

⟫⟫⟫ My Prayer ⟪⟪⟪

For no matter how many **promises God has made,** they are "**Yes**" in Christ. And so through him the "**Amen**" is spoken by us to the glory of God.

2 Corinthians 1:20

Reflection

_____
_____
_____
_____
_____
_____
_____
_____
_____
_____
_____
_____
_____
_____
_____
_____
_____
_____
_____

WHAT I'M Thankful FOR

_____
_____
_____
_____
_____
_____
_____
_____
_____
_____

⟫⟫⟫— My Prayer —⟪⟪⟪

Do you not know that your bodies are temples of the Holy Spirit, who is in you, whom you have received from God? You are not your own; you were **bought** at a price. Therefore honor God with your bodies.

1 CORINTHIANS 6:19-20

Date: ~~~~~~~~~~~~~~~

~~~~~~~~~~~~~~~

Reflection

WHAT I'M Thankful FOR

My Prayer

Therefore I tell you, whatever you **ask for in prayer, believe** that **you have received it**, and it **will be yours.**

Mark 11:24

Date: ~~~~~~~~~~

~~~~~~~~~~

Reflection

_____
_____
_____
_____
_____
_____
_____
_____
_____
_____
_____
_____
_____
_____
_____
_____
_____
_____

WHAT I'M Thankful FOR

_____
_____
_____
_____
_____

_____
_____
_____
_____
_____

My Prayer

But for you who **fear my name**, the Sun of Righteousness will rise with healing in his wings. And you will **go free**, leaping with **joy** like calves let out to pasture.

MALACHI 4:2 (NLT)

Reflection

WHAT I'M Thankful FOR

_____
_____
_____
_____
_____
_____
_____
_____

⟩⟩⟩— My Prayer —⟨⟨⟨

_____
_____
_____
_____
_____
_____
_____
_____
_____

You will **not fear** the **terror** of night, **nor the arrow** that flies by day, **nor the pestilence** that stalks in the darkness, **nor the plague** that destroys at midday.

A thousand may fall at your side, ten thousand at your right hand, but **it will not come near you**.

Psalm 91:5-7

Date: ~~~~~~~~~~~~~~~~~~~~~~~~

~~~~~~~~~~~~~~~~~~~~~~~~

Reflection

_____

_____

_____

_____

_____

_____

_____

_____

_____

_____

_____

_____

_____

_____

_____

_____

_____

_____

WHAT I'M Thankful FOR

My Prayer

God also bound himself with an oath, so that those who received the promise could be perfectly sure that he would never change his mind.

HEBREWS 6:17 (TLB)

Date: ~~~~~~~~~~
~~~~~~~~~~

Reflection

_____

_____

_____

_____

_____

_____

_____

_____

_____

_____

_____

_____

_____

_____

_____

_____

_____

_____

WHAT I'M Thankful FOR

_____
_____
_____
_____
_____
_____
_____
_____
_____

My Prayer

_____
_____
_____
_____
_____
_____
_____
_____

It has come at last— **salvation and power** and the **Kingdom of our God**, and the authority of his Christ. For the accuser of our brothers and sisters has been thrown down to earth—the one who accuses them before our God day and night.

And they have **defeated him** by the **blood of the Lamb** and by their **testimony**.

Revelation 12:10–11b (NLT)

Date: ~~~~~~~~~~~~~~~~~
~~~~~~~~~~~~~~~~~

Reflection

_____
_____
_____
_____
_____
_____
_____
_____
_____
_____
_____
_____
_____
_____
_____
_____
_____
_____
_____

WHAT I'M Thankful FOR

_____
_____
_____
_____
_____
_____
_____
_____
_____

⟫⟩⟩ My Prayer ⟨⟨⟪

_____
_____
_____
_____
_____
_____
_____
_____

I will **exalt you**, Lord,
for you **lifted me** out of the
depths and **did not let** my
enemies gloat over me.

Lord my God, I called to you
for help, and **you healed me**.

You, Lord, **brought me up**
from the realm of the dead;
you **spared me** from going
down to the pit.

Psalm 30:1-3

Reflection

_____

_____

_____

_____

_____

_____

_____

_____

_____

_____

_____

_____

_____

_____

_____

_____

_____

_____

_____

WHAT I'M
Thankful
FOR

_____

_____

_____

_____

_____

_____

_____

_____

_____

_____

My Prayer

_____

_____

_____

_____

_____

_____

_____

_____

Answered Prayers and Testimonies

Words from God to Me

FOR MORE RESOURCES FROM
AMY KEESEE FREUDIGER
ON HEALING AND OTHER
TOPICS FOR YOUR SPIRITUAL
ENCOURAGEMENT, GO TO
HEALEDOVERNIGHT.COM.